Read about Greenbug's adventures
when he goes out to sea in his little
boat. A police boat chases Swifty
Pig, a barge catches fire, the coastguard boat rescues sailors from
sunken motorboats — and lots more!
Don't forget to help Greenbug
look for his friend Goldbug.

Richard Scarry's

Boats

Published in Great Britain with the authorization
of Winthers Forlag A/S by
World International Publishing Ltd., an Egmont Company,
Egmont House, PO Box 111, Great Ducie Street,
Manchester M60 3BL.
Printed in Germany. ISBN 0-7498-0430-0

Greenbug has a little boat. Everywhere he goes, he looks for his friend, Goldbug.

The wind blows on the sails.
It makes the boat go.

Can you find Goldbug in
each picture?

Father Cat is
fishing.
Does he catch a
fish?
Goldbug can see
what he catches.

Oh, no!
The motorboat
drivers aren't looking
where they are going.
The sailors aren't hurt
—just a bit wet.

A big freighter is tied up
at the dock.

It is loaded up with all kinds of things.
It will take them to faraway ports.
Where is Goldbug?

Captain Salty takes his liner
on a cruise.
The passengers eat and sleep on
the liner for many days.

Don't eat too much, Goldbug!

Oh, no!
Another accident!
Two motorboats sink.
The coastguard boat
rescues the sailors.

There are many kinds of boat.
Here are a gondola, a Viking
longboat and a raft.

Can you see Goldbug?

A barge is on fire!
The fireboats put
the fire out.

Huckle Cat, Lowly Worm
and Goldbug are
good firemen.

Some people live on boats.

Submarines travel
on water.
They can also
travel under water.

This family lives on a houseboat.

Fishing boats travel out to sea.

They catch fish for
us to eat.

Swifty Pig goes too fast.
A police boat chases after him.

Look where you are
going, Swifty!

Captain Fishhead has a motorboat.

He takes his friends
for a trip.
Have a good trip,
everyone!